SIRT DIET

igloobooks

Published in 2016
by Igloo Books Ltd
Cottage Farm
Sywell
NN6 0BJ
www.igloobooks.com

Following images are courtesy of Shutterstock:
4 © Anna Bogush/Shutterstock, 7b © 5 second Studio/Shutterstock,
8 © SOMMAI/Shutterstock, 12 ©casanisa/Shutterstock, 28 © TGTGTG/Shutterstock,
46 © Boule/Shutterstock, 62 ©VICUSCHKA/Shutterstock
All additional images ©iStock / Getty

Cover and interiors designed by Nicholas Gage
Edited by Natalie Baker

LEO002 1116
2 4 6 8 10 9 7 5 3 1
ISBN 978-1-78670-255-5

Printed and manufactured in China

Contents

Choosing Sirtfoods

The essence of dieting has often been about what you should exclude from your diet to achieve a certain health benefit, for example, reducing your sugar content, cutting out your carbs or going gluten free.

The Sirt Diet is different. This healthy-eating plan is all about adding certain foods in your diet that are going to have a positive impact on your body, metabolism and general well-being.

The start of Sirtfood

The two health consultants who researched and developed the Sirt Diet, Aiden Goggins and Glen Matten, attributed the term 'sirtfood' to a group of foods that are high in surtuin activators. Their diet plan is based on the theory that proteins in the body, called surtuins (short for Silent Information Regulators, or SIRs), can be activated by various polyphenols found in certain plant-based foods. Surtuins are proteins found in the body that, when stimulated, control a number of body mechanisms, including fat metabolism, cellular survival and inflammation, all of which can be linked to various chronic diseases. This theory is supported by the fact that many of the healthiest nations, such as Japan and Italy, that have low incidences of obesity, diabetes and heart disease, are also known to consume a diet high in sirtfoods.

What are the top Sirtfoods?

Goggins and Matten identified 20 top sirtfoods that contain high levels of surtuin activators. There are a further 40 known food sources that also contain them at lower levels. As you can see from the table below, many of these foods are regular shopping list items but your greatest challenge may be how to incorporate these items into your everyday meals. This is where we come in. This book aims to provide you with the diet plan and some of the recipes and ideas needed to get you started on the Sirt Diet. By the time you have completed Phase 2 of this healthy eating regime, you'll be familiar with foods rich in surtuin-activating properties and have no problem including these in your daily meals. Research has shown that, as well as maintaining a healthy weight, those following a diet high in sirtfoods were more easily able to regulate their appetite, had more energy and showed an increase in muscle mass.

Although the recipes in this book provide ways to increase your sirtfood intake, it is important to maintain a balanced diet. Ensure your diet includes wholegrains, fruit and vegetables, oily fish, beans and lentils, and dairy or dairy alternatives. As well as sirtfoods, your body requires essential macro and micronutrients to provide you with energy, vitamins and minerals to function optimally.

Top 20 Sirtfoods

Birds eye chillies	Coffee	Medjool dates	Rocket
Buckwheat	Extra virgin olive oil	Parsley	Strawberries
Capers	Green tea	Red chicory	Soy
Celery	Kale	Red onion	Turmeric
Cocoa	Lovage	Red wine	Walnuts

Sirtfood science

When we consume a very low-calorie diet, fast or participate in an intensive exercise regime, our body responds in several ways. Firstly, the body activates a gene that turns off mechanisms involved in fat storage and switches to fat burning, hence boosting our metabolism. Secondly, it triggers pathways in the body that aid tissue growth and repair, helping to slow down the ageing process. However, these can have side-effects of low mood and energy slumps – none of which we want to experience when aiming for a healthier lifestyle.

Surtuin activators in Sirtfoods	
Sirtfood	**Surtuin activator**
Green tea	Epigallocatechin-3-gallate (EGCG)
Dark chocolate	Antioxidant – resveratrol
Extra virgin olive oil	Oleuropein
Tofu	Isoflavones
Turmeric	Antioxidant – curcumin
Red onion	Quercetin

Activating sirtuins

Research suggests that the family of genes, known as surtuins, activated by fasting or intense exercise, can also be triggered by consuming sirtfoods. Sirtfoods contain one of a number of phytochemicals known to activate the 'skinny' gene. The seven sirtuin genes that have been identified, SIRT1 to SIRT7, are thought to have various functions within the body. These include metabolism regulation, anti-ageing mechanisms and pathways related to cell and DNA repair.

Further Benefits

Biologists have concluded several studies on the sirtuins and have had positive results relating to increased lifespan, metabolism and anti-ageing. Although most of these studies have been on yeast and mice, and have yet to be carried out on humans, what is becoming apparent is that the sirtuin family of genes is extremely valuable within the body.

Sirtfoods and exercise

Although a diet rich in sirtfoods activates a fat burning reaction in your body, it is important to remember that we cannot rely on foods alone to keep us healthy.

Exercise not only helps to burn fat but it also builds muscle, keeps our heart and circulation healthy and provides us with a sense of emotional wellbeing. Research suggests that regular moderate to high intensity exercise is more effective than anti-depressant medications in lifting our spirits and making us feel good, so why wouldn't we want to continue to do that?

Try to incorporate regular exercise into your daily routine by finding something that you enjoy doing. You do not have to be pounding weights at the gym or trying to follow the new dance class moves. Brisk walking with friends or joining a team game will not only keep you fit but it will also keep you connected with others.

Sirtfood planning

Although the Sirt Diet is calorie-restricted at the beginning, it is all about a long-term solution to maintaining a fit and healthy body. When developing the Sirt Diet, Goggins and Matten included a mild fasting element at the start of the programme to kick-start your metabolism and make it easier for the surtuin activators to do their job.

The research carried out by these nutritional experts suggests that you could lose up to 3 kilograms (7 pounds) in the first week. After this, it is all about including more sirtfoods in your daily routine. Below is a step-by-step guide to preparing for your sirtfood journey.

Phase 1
The first three days of the programme are the most calorie-restricted part, made up of three green juices plus one sirt-rich meal, all containing less than 1000 kcal. In the clinical trials of this diet, participants were not found to feel excessively hungry or experience any side effects. However, you should always check with your GP before embarking on any calorie-restricted diet and stop if you experience unexpected side effects. For days four to seven, the calorie restriction is increased to 1500 kcal each day as one of the green juices is replaced with an additional sirt-rich meal.

Phase 2
For the following two weeks, you'll be eating three regular sirtfood-rich meals each day and supplementing this with a daily green smoothie boost. You may notice that you continue to lose weight during this phase but the weight loss will be less rapid. During these two weeks, try to focus on the recipes you're using from the book and how you might be able to adapt or add to these once you continue to maintain your new healthy-eating regime.

Maintenance
Once you've finished Phase 2, you'll be familiar with the top 20 sirtfoods and may even be including other sirtfoods in your daily recipes. To consolidate your new healthy-eating habits, it is useful to find ways to incorporate some of these sirtfoods into your daily routine so the food preparation becomes easy and effortless. This may include having a coffee with your breakfast or adding turmeric to your boiled rice.

Phase 1

	Day 1	Day 2	Day 3	Day 4	Day 5	Day 6	Day 7
Breakfast	Super Green Juice p.25	Super Green Juice p.25	Super Green Juice p.25	Super Green Juice p.25	Tropical Smoothie p.20	Cacao Morning Smoothie P.23	Super Green Juice p.25
Lunch	Super Green Juice p.25	Super Green Juice p.25	Super Green Juice p.25	Squash and Feta Salad p.38	Pear, Walnut and Rocket Salad p.72	Citrus-cured Salmon on Rye p.35	Fruity Roquefort Salad p.76
Dinner	Plaice with Avocado Salsa p.39	Vegetable Buckwheat Pizza p.43	Roast Chicken with Quinoa p.31	Stuffed Sweet Potato p.41	Halibut with Kale and Capers p.30	Soba Noodle Salad p.42	Chicken Udon Stir-fry p.36
Treat	Super Green Juice p.25	Super Green Juice p.25	Super Green Juice p.25	Raw Raspberry Tarts p.52	Matcha Chia Pudding p.54	Cacao Blueberry Pudding p.56	Walnut Brownies p.48

Breakfast

Turbocharge your whole body by beginning the day with a nutritious breakfast! Breakfast is very important as it sets you up for the day ahead. Time may be of the essence, but it really is easy to incorporate sirt-rich foods into this first meal. As described in the opening chapters, after the initial stage of fasting and juicing recommended with this diet, the focus shifts to eating 'normally' again, but increasing your intake of the healthy recommended sirtfoods. These breakfast recipes provide some deliciously juicy, sirt-packed blends to kick-start the programme followed by some more substantial suggestions once that initial 3-day detox has been done. Packed with chia seeds and fresh fruit, the **Tropical Smoothie** works well as a fast, sirt-rich breakfast. Meanwhile, if you're after a more substantial meal, the delicious **Blueberry Pancakes** can keep you feeling full for hours. Incorporating such succulent treats as strawberries, blueberries and walnuts has never sounded so mouth-watering as a breakfast menu! You may be surprised by how tantalisingly tasty a sirtuin-packed breakfast can be!

Blueberry Pancakes

SERVES: 4 PREP. TIME: 10 MINS COOKING TIME: 30 MINS

INGREDIENTS

250 g / 9 oz / 1 ⅔ cups plain (all-purpose)
flour

2 tsp baking powder

2 very ripe bananas

2 large eggs

225 ml / 8 fl. oz / ¾ cups milk

2 tbsp melted butter

100 g / 3 ½ oz / ⅔ cup blueberries

a few sprigs mint

maple syrup to serve

METHOD

- Mix the flour and baking powder in a bowl and make a well in the centre.
- Mash the bananas with a fork until smooth, then whisk in the eggs and milk. Gradually whisk the mixture into the flour bowl.
- Melt the butter in a frying pan then whisk it into the batter. Put the buttered frying pan back over a low heat.
- Spoon heaped tablespoons of the batter into the pan, sprinkle a few blueberries on top and cook for 2 minutes or until small bubbles start to appear on the surface. Turn the pancakes over with a spatula and cook the other side until golden brown and cooked through.
- Repeat until all the batter has been used, keeping the finished batches warm in a low oven.
- Serve with mint sprigs, the rest of the blueberries and a drizzle of maple syrup.

Chia Panna Cotta

SERVES: **6** PREP. TIME: **10 MINS** CHILLING TIME: **4 HOURS**

INGREDIENTS

75 ml / 2 ½ fl. oz / ⅓ cup agave nectar

900 ml / 1 ½ pint / 3 ½ cups soya milk

150 g / 5 ½ oz / ¾ cup chia seeds

1 tsp vanilla extract

50 g / 1 ¾ oz / ½ cup dried banana chips, chopped

6 strawberries, chopped

50 g / 1 ¾ oz / ¼ cup goji berries

50 g / 1 ¾ oz / ¼ cup dried (unsweetened) cranberries

6 sprigs mint

METHOD

• Dissolve the agave nectar in the soya milk, then stir in the chia seeds and vanilla extract.

• Cover and chill in the fridge for 4 hours or ideally overnight.

• Stir the chia mixture then spoon it into six glasses and top with the rest of the ingredients.

Blueberry and Walnut Muffins

MAKES: **12** PREP. TIME: **25 MINS** COOKING TIME: **20 MINS**

INGREDIENTS

1 large egg

120 ml / 4 fl. oz / ½ cup sunflower oil

2 tbsp orange juice

120 ml / 4 fl. oz / ½ cup milk

375 g / 12 ½ oz / 2 ½ cups self-raising flour, sifted

1 tsp baking powder

200 g / 7 oz / ¾ cup caster (superfine) sugar

150 g / 5 oz / 1 cup blueberries, plus extra to garnish

50 g / 1 ¾ oz / ½ cup walnuts, chopped

1 orange, zest finely grated

METHOD

- Preheat the oven to 180°C (160°C fan) / 350F / gas 4 and line a 12-hole muffin tin with paper cases.
- Beat the egg in a jug with the oil, orange juice and milk until well mixed.
- Mix the flour, baking powder, sugar, blueberries, walnuts and orange zest in a bowl, then pour in the egg mixture and stir just enough to combine.
- Divide the mixture between the cases, then bake in the oven for 20 minutes. Test with a wooden toothpick, if it comes out clean, the cakes are done. If not, test again in 5 minutes.
- Transfer the cakes to a wire rack and leave to cool completely, then garnish with blueberries.

Buckwheat Goji Granola

SERVES: **6** PREP. TIME: **5 MINS** COOKING TIME: **1 HOUR**

INGREDIENTS

75 ml / 2 ½ fl. oz / ⅓ cup maple syrup

75 ml / 2 ½ fl. oz / ⅓ cup apple juice

1 tbsp extra virgin olive oil

175 g / 6 oz / 1 ¾ cups rolled buckwheat flakes

100 g / 3 ½ oz / ¾ cup walnuts, chopped

75 g / 2 ½ oz / 1 cup flaked almonds

50 g / 1 ¾ oz / ½ cup sunflower seeds

600 ml / 1 pint / 2 ½ cups soya yogurt

200 g / 7 oz / 1 cup goji berries

6 large strawberries, halved

METHOD

- Preheat the oven to 160°C (140°C fan) / 325F / gas 3.
- Stir the maple syrup, apple juice and oil together in a bowl with a pinch of salt then toss it with the buckwheat flakes, walnuts, almonds and seeds.
- Spread the mixture out on a large baking tray and bake for 1 hour, stirring every 10 minutes to ensure it all toasts evenly. Leave the granola to cool completely, then store in an airtight jar.
- Divide the granola between six bowls and serve with soya yogurt, goji berries and strawberries.

Avocado Smoothie Bowl

SERVES: **2** PREP. TIME: **5 MINS** COOKING TIME: **0 MINS**

INGREDIENTS

250 ml / 9 fl. oz / 1 cup soya milk

250 ml / 9 fl. oz / 1 cup apple juice

2 ripe avocados, peeled, stoned and chopped

1 banana, sliced

1 small handful mint leaves, plus 2 sprigs to garnish

1 tbsp matcha green tea powder

2 tbsp coconut sugar

8 ice cubes

50 g / 1 ¾ oz / ¼ cup dried cranberries

28 g / 1 oz / ¼ cup shredded coconut

2 tbsp chia seeds

METHOD

- Put the soya milk, apple juice, avocado, banana, mint, matcha and coconut sugar in a liquidizer and blend until very smooth.
- Add the ice cubes and blend again until smooth.
- Pour the soup into two bowls and top with cranberries, coconut, chia seeds and mint sprigs.

Tropical Smoothie

SERVES: **2** PREP. TIME: **15 MINS** COOKING TIME: **0 MINS**

INGREDIENTS

2 tbsp chia seeds

250 ml / 9 fl. oz / 1 cup soya milk

¼ very ripe pineapple, peeled, cored and chopped

1 ripe mango, peeled, stoned and chopped

2 bananas, sliced

2 tbsp desiccated coconut

1 tsp ground turmeric

8 ice cubes

METHOD

- Stir the chia seeds into the soya milk and leave to thicken for 10 minutes.
- Transfer to a liquidizer with the rest of the ingredients and blend until very smooth.
- Pour into two bottles or glasses and serve immediately.

Cacao and Banana Porridge

SERVES: 4 PREP. TIME: 10 MINS COOKING TIME: 5 MINS

INGREDIENTS

100 g / 3 ½ oz / 1 cup buckwheat porridge flakes

600 ml / 1 pint / 2 ½ cups soya milk

2 tsp honey

50 ml / 1 ¾ fl. oz / ¼ cup coconut milk

50 g / 1 ¾ oz / 1/3 cup dark chocolate (minimum 85% cocoa solids), finely chopped

1 large banana, sliced

2 tbsp cocoa nibs

2 tbsp pumpkin seeds

1 handful blueberries

1 tsp chia seeds

METHOD

- Put the buckwheat flakes, soya milk and honey in a saucepan. Simmer for 4 minutes, stirring occasionally, until thick.

- Meanwhile, heat the coconut milk and chocolate together in a small pan over a low heat until melted and smooth.

- Divide the porridge between two warm bowls and top with the banana, cocoa nibs and pumpkin seeds.

- Drizzle over the chocolate sauce and top with blueberries and chia seeds.

Cacao Morning Smoothie

SERVES: 2 PREP. TIME: 25 MINS COOKING TIME: 0 MINS

INGREDIENTS

50 g / 1 ¾ oz / ¼ cup chia seeds

28 g / 1 oz / ¼ cup buckwheat porridge flakes

500 ml / 17 ½ fl. oz / 2 cups almond milk

2 bananas, sliced and frozen for at least 2 hours

2 tbsp pure cacao powder

1 tsp ground turmeric

1 tbsp golden linseeds

4 medjool dates, stoned and chopped

METHOD

- Stir the chia seeds and buckwheat flakes into the almond milk and leave to thicken for 20 minutes.
- Transfer to a liquidizer with the rest of the ingredients and blend until very smooth.
- Pour into two bottles or glasses and serve immediately.

Super Green Juice

MAKES: **2 large glasses** PREP. TIME: **5 MINS** FREEZING TIME: **2 HOURS**

INGREDIENTS

150 g / 5 ½ oz / 1 cup blueberries

150 g / 5 ½ oz / 1 cup ripe mango, cubed

2 bananas, chopped

35 g / 1 ¼ oz / 1 cup kale

35 g / 1 ¼ oz / 1 cup flat-leaf parsley

4 medjool dates, stoned and chopped

250 ml / 9 fl. oz / 1 cup soya milk

250 ml / 9 fl. oz / 1 cup apple juice

1 lime, juiced

METHOD

- Spread the blueberries, mango and banana out on a greaseproof paper lined baking tray and freeze for at least 2 hours. The fruit can then be transferred to a freezer bag and stored for future use or used straight away.

- Put the kale, parsley and dates in a liquidizer with the soya milk, apple juice and lime juice. Blend until smooth.

- Add the frozen fruit and blend again until smooth, then pour into glasses or bottles and serve immediately.

Layered Buckwheat Porridge

SERVES: 4 PREP. TIME: 5 MINS COOKING TIME: 10 MINS

INGREDIENTS

75 g / 2 ½ oz / ½ cup blueberries

500 ml / 17 ½ fl. oz / 2 cups apple juice

200 g / 7 oz / 2 cups buckwheat porridge flakes

600 ml / 1 pint / 2 ½ cups soya milk

2 tbsp coconut sugar

50 g / 1 ¾ oz / ½ cup pure cacao powder

2 large bananas, sliced

2 tbsp almonds, chopped

METHOD

- Put the blueberries and apple juice in a saucepan and simmer for 2 minutes. Blend until smooth with an immersion blender.

- Add half of the buckwheat flakes and simmer for 4 minutes, stirring occasionally.

- Meanwhile, put the rest of the buckwheat flakes in a second saucepan with the soya milk, sugar and cacao powder. Simmer for 4 minutes, stirring occasionally until thick.

- Divide the blueberry porridge between four pots, then press a layer of banana round the inside. Top with the cacao porridge and sprinkle with chopped almonds. Serve immediately.

Chia Granola Pots

SERVES: 6 PREP. TIME: 15 MINS COOKING TIME: 1 HOUR CHILLING TIME: 4 HOURS

INGREDIENTS

50 ml / 1 ¾ fl. oz / ¼ cup runny honey

600 ml / 1 pint / 2 ½ cups soya milk

100 g / 3 ½ oz / ½ cup chia seeds

75 ml / 2 ½ fl. oz / ⅓ cup maple syrup

75 ml / 2 ½ fl. oz / ⅓ cup apple juice

1 tbsp extra virgin olive oil

175 g / 6 oz / 1 ¾ cups rolled buckwheat flakes

100 g / 3 ½ oz / ¾ cup walnuts, chopped

150 g / 5 ½ oz / 1 cup blueberries

METHOD

- Dissolve the honey in the soya milk, then stir in the chia seeds. Cover and chill in the fridge for 4 hours or ideally overnight.

- Preheat the oven to 160°C (140°C fan) / 325F / gas 3.

- Stir the maple syrup, apple juice and oil together in a bowl with a pinch of salt then toss it with the buckwheat flakes and walnuts.

- Spread out the mixture on a large baking tray and bake for 1 hour, stirring every 10 minutes to ensure it all toasts evenly. Leave the granola to cool completely, then store in an airtight jar.

- When you're ready to serve, spoon a little granola into the bottom of six small glasses or jars. Stir the chia mixture and spoon it on top, then add a little more granola and top with blueberries.

Mains

Lunch and dinnertime meals can vary enormously based on how much time is available to prepare and eat food. Because of this, there is a wide range of options in the following recipes to allow you to pick and choose the appropriate meals depending on your time-constraints and lifestyle. From soups or salads to hearty, nutrition-packed dinners, you'll discover that the so-called 'wonderfoods' can easily be incorporated. These foods will activate proteins in the body called sirtuins and can help to protect your metabolic health. Tasty meals that contain extra virgin olive oil, kale and red onion, for example, all provide a great source of energy-rich nourishment, in turn offering all-round health benefits. Main meals such as the **Chicken Udon Stir-Fry** and **Stuffed Sweet Potato** are brilliant for keeping your energy levels up, and allow you to get on with your day without the worry of being hungry. With this diet, the occasional glass of red wine is actively encouraged which is a great accompaniment to some of the recipes, and an acceptable treat to enjoy at dinner time!

Halibut with Kale and Capers

SERVES: **4** PREP. TIME: **5 MINS** COOKING TIME: **15 MINS**

INGREDIENTS

4 thick portions halibut fillet

6 tbsp extra virgin olive oil

1 leek, sliced

2 cloves of garlic, sliced

300 g / 10 ½ oz / 9 cups baby kale, chopped

75 ml / 2 ½ fl. oz / ⅓ cup dry white wine

150 g / 5 ½ oz / 1 cup cherry tomatoes, quartered

75 g / 2 ½ oz / ½ cup mixed kalamata and green olives, stoned and chopped

75 g / 2 ½ oz / ⅓ cup capers, rinsed and drained

50 g / 1 ¾ oz / ½ cup pine nuts, toasted

1 lemon, cut into wedges

METHOD

- Preheat the oven to 160°C (140°C fan) / 325F / gas 3 and heat a griddle pan until smoking hot.

- Brush the halibut with 2 tbsp of the oil and season with salt and pepper. Sear the halibut on both sides in the hot griddle pan, then transfer to a roasting tin and cook in the oven for 8 minutes. When the time is up, wrap the roasting tin in a double layer of foil and leave to rest in a warm place.

- While the fish is cooking, heat 3 tbsp of oil in a large sauté pan and sauté the leek and garlic for 5 minutes. Add the kale and stir well, then pour in the wine and cover with the lid. Cook the kale for 5 minutes, stirring occasionally, then season with salt and pepper.

- While the kale is cooking, heat the final tbsp of oil in a frying pan and fry the tomatoes, olives and capers together until the tomatoes start to soften. Stir in the pine nuts.

- Divide the kale between four warm plates and top with the halibut fillets. Scatter over the tomato mixture and serve with lemon wedges to squeeze over at the table.

Roast Chicken with Quinoa

SERVES: 4 PREP. TIME: **5 MINS** COOKING TIME: **25 MINS**

INGREDIENTS

150 g / 5 ½ oz / ¾ cup red quinoa

250 g / 9 oz / 1 ¼ cups jasmine rice

750 ml / 1 pint 5 ½ fl. oz / 3 cups chicken stock

4 chicken breasts

4 tbsp extra virgin olive oil

1 tbsp Cajun seasoning

1 red pepper, diced

1 yellow pepper, diced

1 green pepper, diced

200 g / 7 oz / 1 cup canned kidney beans, rinsed and drained

1 small handful curly parsley, chopped

METHOD

- Preheat the oven to 200°C (180°C fan) / 400F / gas 6.
- Put the quinoa, rice and stock in a saucepan. When the stock starts boiling, cover the pan, reduce the heat and simmer gently for 10 minutes. Leave to stand off the heat for 15 minutes, without lifting the lid.
- Meanwhile, brush the chicken with half the oil and sprinkle with Cajun seasoning. Roast the chicken for 20 minutes or until cooked through. Cover with foil and leave to rest in a warm place.
- Heat the rest of the oil in a large sauté pan and sauté the peppers and kidney beans for 5 minutes. Fluff up the rice with a fork, then toss it with the peppers and parsley.
- Divide the rice between four warm plates. Slice the chicken breasts and arrange on top, then serve immediately.

Squash and Chickpea Soup

SERVES: **6** PREP. TIME: **10 MINS** COOKING TIME: **35 MINS**

INGREDIENTS

6 tbsp extra virgin olive oil

1 red onion, finely chopped

2 celery sticks, finely chopped

2 cloves of garlic, finely chopped

1 tsp ground cumin

1 tsp ground turmeric

½ tsp chilli (chili) flakes

1 large butternut squash, peeled, deseeded and cut into chunks

1 litre / 1 pint 15 fl. oz / 4 cups vegetable stock

400 g / 14 oz / 2 cups canned chickpeas (garbanzo beans), drained

1 small bunch dill, finely chopped

METHOD

- Heat half the oil in a large saucepan and fry the onion, celery and garlic for 5 minutes to soften without colouring.

- Add the spices and squash to the pan and stir to coat in the oil, then pour in the stock and bring to the boil. Reduce the heat a little and simmer for 25 minutes or until the squash is tender.

- Blend the soup until smooth, using a liquidizer or immersion blender, then taste and adjust the seasoning.

- Heat the rest of the oil in a small saucepan and cook the chickpeas until piping hot. Stir in the dill.

- Ladle the soup into six warm bowls and top with the chickpea mixture.

Rice and Tofu Congee

SERVES: 4 PREP. TIME: 5 MINS COOKING TIME: 45 MINS

INGREDIENTS

3 tbsp coconut oil

1 red onion, finely chopped

200 g / 7 oz / 1 cup red rice

400 ml / 14 fl. oz / 1 ⅔ cups vegetable stock

1 leek, thinly sliced

1 tbsp yellow curry paste

1 bay leaf

350 g / 12 oz / 1 ½ cups firm tofu, cubed

100 g / 3 ½ ox / 1 ⅓ cups button mushrooms, quartered

400 ml / 14 fl. oz / 2 cups coconut milk

100 g / 3 ½ ox / ½ cup green beans, halved

75 g / 2 ½ oz / ½ cup peas, defrosted if frozen

50 g / 1 ¾ oz / 1 ½ cups baby leaf spinach

1–2 tbsp soy sauce

METHOD

- Put half the coconut oil in a saucepan and fry the onion for 5 minutes to soften without colouring. Stir in the rice and stock, then cover and simmer for 40 minutes, stirring occasionally.

- When the rice has been cooking for 20 minutes, heat the rest of the coconut oil in a wok and fry the leek over a low heat for 5 minutes.

- Stir in the curry paste and bay leaf then increase the heat and fry for 2 minutes. Add the tofu and mushrooms and toss to coat.

- Pour in the coconut milk and simmer gently for 5 minutes. Add the beans and peas and simmer for 4 minutes, then stir in the spinach and add soy sauce to taste.

- When the rice is tender, divide between four warm bowls and top with the braised tofu.

Citrus-cured Salmon on Rye

SERVES: **4** PREP. TIME: **30 MINS** COOKING TIME: **0 MINS**

INGREDIENTS

350 g / 12 oz very fresh salmon fillet in one piece

1 tbsp sea salt

1 red onion, sliced

3 limes, juiced

1 clementine, juiced

4 large slices rye bread

100 g / 3 ½ oz / ½ cup cream cheese

2 avocados, peeled, stoned and sliced

½ tsp herbes de Provence

METHOD

- Sprinkle the salmon with the salt and chill for 15 minutes. Rinse off the salt and dry thoroughly with kitchen paper.

- Arrange the sliced onion in a non-metallic dish. Thinly slice the salmon and arrange on top. Whisk the lime and clementine juices together and pour over the top, then transfer to the fridge to cure for 10 minutes.

- Meanwhile, spread the rye bread with cream cheese and top with avocado.

- Remove the salmon from the curing mixture and arrange it on top, then sprinkle with herbes de Provence and black pepper. Cut each open sandwich into four pieces and serve immediately.

Chicken Udon Stir-fry

SERVES: 4 PREP. TIME: 35 MINS COOKING TIME: 40 MINS

INGREDIENTS

2 large chicken breasts, cut into chunks

1 tbsp red curry paste

4 tbsp extra virgin olive oil

150 g / 5 ½ oz / ¾ cup red quinoa

300 g / 10 ½ oz wholewheat udon noodles

1 red pepper, sliced

1 tbsp soy sauce

150 g / 5 ½ oz / 4 ½ cups spinach leaves, chopped if large

METHOD

- Toss the chicken with the curry paste and half the oil and leave to marinate for 30 minutes.
- Meanwhile, put the quinoa in a saucepan with 150 ml water. Cover and simmer gently for 10 minutes, then leave to stand off the heat for a further 15 minutes without lifting the lid.
- Cook the noodles according to the packet instructions, then refresh in cold water and drain well.
- Heat the rest of the oil in a large wok and stir-fry the chicken for 4 minutes. Add the pepper and stir-fry for 2 minutes, then add the quinoa and noodles.
- Continue to stir-fry until piping hot, then take the pan off the heat and stir in the soy sauce and spinach. Serve immediately.

Squash and Feta Salad

SERVES: 4 PREP. TIME: 10 MINS COOKING TIME: 35 MINS

INGREDIENTS

1 butternut squash, peeled, deseeded and cubed

5 tbsp extra virgin olive oil

1 broccoli, divided into small florets

300 g / 10 ½ oz / 1 ¾ cups couscous

1 lemon, juiced

75 g / 2 ½ oz / ⅓ cup feta cheese, crumbled

1 handful baby chard leaves

METHOD

- Preheat the oven to 200°C (180°C fan) / 400F / gas 6.
- Toss the squash cubes with 2 tbsp of the oil in a large baking dish. Cover the dish with foil and bake for 35 minutes or until the squash is tender.
- Towards the end of the cooking time, pour 300 ml of boiling water over the couscous then cover and leave to steam for 5 minutes.
- Meanwhile, steam the broccoli for 4 minutes or until just tender.
- Fluff up the couscous grains with a fork. Whisk the rest of the oil with the lemon juice and a big pinch of salt, then toss with the couscous, squash and broccoli.
- Divide between four warm plates and scatter over the feta and baby chard leaves.

Plaice with Avocado Salsa

SERVES: **2** PREP. TIME: **15 MINS** COOKING TIME: **6 MINS**

INGREDIENTS

2 oranges

2 ripe avocados, halved and stoned

4 tbsp olive oil

2 plaice fillets

1 tbsp flat-leaf parsley, chopped

1 tbsp lovage, chopped

½ lime

METHOD

- Slice the top and bottom off the oranges. Slice away the peel then cut out each individual segment, leaving the white pith behind like the pages of a book. Squeeze the pith over a bowl to collect the juice.
- Scoop the avocado flesh out of the skins and cut it into cubes then douse it with the reserved orange juice to prevent discolouration.
- Heat half the oil in a large frying pan. Season the fish with salt and pepper, then fry it gently for 3 minutes on each side or until just cooked through.
- Gently toss the avocado with the orange segments, parsley and lovage and dress it with the rest of the olive oil and the juice of half a lime. Serve with the fish.

Stuffed Sweet Potato

SERVES: **4** PREP. TIME: **5 MINS** COOKING TIME: **45 MINS**

INGREDIENTS

4 sweet potatoes

300 g / 9 oz / 1 ½ cups red and wild rice mix

3 tbsp extra virgin olive oil

2 tsp fresh root ginger, finely chopped

½ tsp chilli (chili) flakes

75 g / 2 ½ oz / ⅔ cup walnuts, chopped

50 g / 1 ¾ oz / ⅓ cup pumpkin seeds

8 medjool dates, stoned and chopped

2 tbsp dark soy sauce

METHOD

- Preheat the oven to 200°C (180°C fan) / 400F / gas 6. Bake the sweet potatoes for 45 minutes or until a skewer slides in easily.
- Meanwhile, put the rice in a large saucepan with 1 ½ litres of water. Cover and simmer gently for 30 minutes or until cooked, then drain well.
- Heat the oil in a large sauté pan and fry the ginger and chilli for 2 minutes. Add the walnuts and pumpkin seeds and sauté for 2 more minutes, then stir in the rice, dates and soy sauce.
- Cut open the sweet potatoes and transfer to four warm plates, then spoon the rice mixture on top. Serve immediately.

Soba Noodle Salad

SERVES: **4** PREP. TIME: **15 MINS** COOKING TIME: **5 MINS**

INGREDIENTS

300 g / 10 ½ oz buckwheat soba noodles

2 carrots, peeled and julienned

¼ red cabbage, thinly sliced

4 spring onions (scallions), sliced

1 small bunch coriander (cilantro), leaves picked

FOR THE DRESSING:

1 tbsp caster (superfine) sugar

2 tbsp rice wine vinegar

2 tbsp light soy sauce

1 lime, juiced

1 tbsp sesame oil

1 clove of garlic, crushed

2 tsp fresh root ginger, finely grated

1 tbsp sesame seeds, toasted

METHOD

- Cook the noodles according to the packet instructions, then refresh in cold water and drain well. Toss the noodles with the carrots, red cabbage and spring onions.

- To make the dressing, stir the sugar into the vinegar until it dissolves, then stir in the rest of the dressing ingredients.

- Pour the dressing all over the salad and mix well. Leave to stand for 10 minutes to allow the flavours to develop and the vegetables to soften.

- Add the coriander leaves, toss once more and serve.

Vegetable Buckwheat Pizza

SERVES: **4** PREP. TIME: **20 MINS** COOKING TIME: **15 MINS**

INGREDIENTS

225 g / 8 oz / 1 ½ cups wholegrain buckwheat flour

50 g / 1 ¾ oz / ½ cup walnuts, finely chopped

2 tbsp chia seeds

1 tsp baking powder

½ tsp sea salt

50 g / 1 ¾ oz / ¼ cup pickled Jalapenos, finely chopped

175 ml / 6 fl. oz / ⅔ cup soya yogurt

3 tomatoes, sliced

4 mushrooms, sliced

1 small red onion, sliced and separated into rings

½ red pepper, sliced

1 handful basil leaves

75 g / 2 ½ oz / ¾ cup goats' cheese, crumbled

METHOD

- Preheat the oven to 190°C (170°C fan) / 375F / gas 5.
- Mix the buckwheat flour with the walnuts, chia seeds, baking powder and salt. Stir together the jalapenos and yogurt, then incorporate it into the flour mixture. Add a little water if needed to bring the mixture into a dough.
- Press or roll the dough into a large oval on top of a sheet of greaseproof paper. Transfer it to a baking tray and bake for 5 minutes.
- Arrange the tomatoes on top in a single layer, then scatter over the mushrooms, onions, peppers, basil and goats' cheese.
- Bake the pizza for 10 minutes or until the base is cooked through.

Kale and Lovage Soup

SERVES: **4** PREP. TIME: **10 MINS** COOKING TIME: **30 MINS**

INGREDIENTS

4 tbsp extra virgin olive oil

2 leeks, halved and sliced

2 cloves of garlic, crushed

3 medium potatoes, peeled and diced

1 litre / 1 pint 15 fl. oz / 4 cups vegetable stock

200 g / 7 oz / 4 cups young kale, chopped

1 small handful lovage leaves

1 small handful curly parsley leaves, plus extra to garnish

50 g / 1 ¾ oz / ½ cup Parmesan, finely grated

croutons to serve

METHOD

- Heat the oil in a saucepan. Set aside a small handful of sliced leek to use as a garnish then fry the rest for 8 minutes or until softened.
- Add the garlic and potatoes to the pan and cook for 2 more minutes, then stir in the vegetable stock and bring to the boil.
- Simmer for 10 minutes then add the kale and cook for a further 5 minutes or until the potatoes are tender. Stir in the lovage, parsley and Parmesan, then transfer the soup to a liquidizer and blend until smooth.
- Taste the soup and adjust the seasoning with salt and pepper, then ladle into bowls and garnish with parsley, sliced leek and croutons.

Desserts

A diet that allows, and even embraces, the use of dark chocolate has got to be an incentive to maintaining a sirt-rich regime – if, indeed, you like chocolate! While this diet may supercharge weight loss, boost memory powers and even help to stave off diseases, there is still space for dessert! The following dessert recipes provide some mouth-watering suggestions, incorporating such delights as berries, walnuts and dark chocolate! It is worth noting that this is not just any chocolate, of course, but the pure, unadulterated sort containing a minimum of seventy per cent cocoa solids. While the colourful **Blueberry Cheesecake** will add some fruitiness to your dessert choice, the more unusual, sirt-rich **Matcha Chia Puddings** and **Whipped Cacao Mousses** will be the perfect accompaniment to a glass of red wine or coffee. Coffee itself is encouraged on this powerful diet and, apart from it being a nice way to finish off a meal, roasted beans or granules can also be incorporated into some delectable desserts.

Walnut Brownies

MAKES: 9 PREP. TIME: 5 MINS COOKING TIME: 35 MINS

INGREDIENTS

100 g / 3 ½ oz / ⅔ cup dark chocolate (minimum 85% cocoa solids), chopped

85 g / 3 oz / ¾ cup pure cacao powder

225 g / 8 oz / 1 cup coconut oil

450 g / 1 lb / 2 ½ cups coconut sugar

4 large eggs

8 medjool dates, stoned and very finely chopped

100 g / 3 ½ oz / ⅔ cup buckwheat flour

75 g / 2 ½ oz / ½ cup walnuts, chopped

METHOD

- Preheat the oven to 160°C (140°C fan) / 325F / gas 3 and oil and line a 20 cm (8 in) square cake tin with greaseproof paper.
- Melt the chocolate, cacao and coconut oil together in a saucepan, then leave to cool a little.
- Whisk the sugar, eggs and dates together with an electric whisk for 3 minutes or until very light and creamy.
- Pour in the chocolate mixture and sieve over the flour, then fold everything together with the walnuts.
- Scrape the mixture into the tin and bake for 35 minutes or until the outside is set, but the centre is still quite soft.
- Leave the brownie to cool completely before cutting and serving.

Pomegranate Chia Verrines

SERVES: **8** PREP. TIME: **40 MINS** COOKING TIME: **4 HOURS**

INGREDIENTS

100 g / 3 ½ oz / ⅔ cup strawberries, sliced
75 ml / 2 ½ fl. oz / ⅓ cup runny honey
900 ml / 1 ½ pint / 3 ½ cups soya milk
150 g / 5 ½ oz / ¾ cup chia seeds
2 pomegranates, seeds only

FOR THE ICE CREAM:
150 g / 5 ½ oz / 1 cup strawberries, sliced
125 g / 4 ½ oz / ⅔ cup coconut sugar
300 ml / 1 ¼ cups coconut milk

METHOD

- First make the ice cream. Mix the strawberries with the sugar and leave to macerate for 30 minutes. Transfer to a liquidizer and blend with the coconut milk until smooth.
- Churn in an ice cream machine according to the manufacturer's instructions, then freeze until you're ready to serve.
- To make the chia layer, put the strawberries, honey and soya milk in a liquidizer and blend until smooth. Stir in the chia seeds, then cover and chill in the fridge for 4 hours or ideally overnight.
- Scoop the ice cream into eight small glasses. Stir the chia mixture, then spoon it on top of the ice cream. Top with pomegranate seeds and serve immediately.

Whipped Cacao Mousse

SERVES: **6** PREP. TIME: **10 MINS** COOKING TIME: **5 MINS** CHILLING TIME: **4 HOURS**

INGREDIENTS

150 g / 5 ½ oz / 1 cup dark chocolate
(min 85% cocoa solids), finely chopped

60 g / 2 oz / ⅔ cup pure cacao powder

125 g / 4 ½ oz / ¾ cup coconut sugar

50 ml / 1 ¾ fl. oz / ¼ cup walnut oil

½ tsp almond extract

450 g / 1 lb / 1 ¾ cups silken tofu

2 tbsp pistachio nuts, chopped

METHOD

- Put the chocolate, cacao, sugar and oil in a bain-marie with 50 ml water and stir until melted and smooth.
- Transfer the mixture to a food processor and add the almond extract and tofu, then blend until very smooth.
- Spoon the mixture into six glasses and chill for at least 4 hours.
- Sprinkle the pistachio nuts on top just before serving.

Raw Raspberry Tarts

MAKES: 12 PREP. TIME: 45 MINS FREEZING TIME: 3 HOURS

INGREDIENTS

250 g / 9 oz / 1 ½ cups medjool dates, stoned

225 g / 8 oz / 1 ¾ cups walnuts, chopped

2 tbsp pure cacao powder

250 g / 9 oz / 1 ⅔ cups raw cashew nuts, soaked overnight

400 ml / 14 fl. oz / 2 cup canned coconut milk, chilled unopened

3 limes, juiced and zest finely grated

75 g / 2 ½ oz / ¼ cup runny honey

200 g / 7 oz / 1 ⅓ cups raspberries

METHOD

- Soak the dates in warm water for 10 minutes, then drain and transfer to a food processor with the walnuts and cacao. Pulse to form a dough, then press into the cups of a 12-hole silicone cupcake mould.
- Drain the cashews and transfer to the food processor. Open the can of coconut milk upside down and discard the thin watery layer. Scoop the thick creamy layer into the food processor and add the lime juice, zest and honey.
- Blend until very smooth. Spoon half of the mixture into the cup cake mould to half-fill the cups.
- Add half of the raspberries to the food processor and blend until smooth. Fill the cupcake mould, then level the tops and cover with cling film.
- Freeze for at least 3 hours. Unmould the tarts 20 minutes before serving to allow them to come up to room temperature. Garnish with the rest of the raspberries.

Berry Ice Lollies

MAKES: **8** PREP. TIME: **15 MINS** FREEZING TIME: **4 HOURS**

INGREDIENTS

200 g / 7 oz / ¾ cup silken tofu

200 ml / 7 fl. oz / ¾ cup coconut milk

1 lemon, juiced

100 g / 3 ½ oz / ½ cup caster (superfine) sugar

100 g / 3 ½ oz / ⅔ cup strawberries, hulled

100 g / 3 ½ oz / ⅔ cup blueberries

METHOD

- Put the tofu, coconut milk, lemon juice and sugar in a liquidizer and blend until smooth.
- Pour half of the mixture into an 8-hole ice lolly mould.
- Add the strawberries to the rest of the mixture in the liquidizer and blend until smooth. Divide two thirds of the mixture between the lolly moulds.
- Add the blueberries to the liquidizer and blend until smooth, then divide between the moulds. Add lolly sticks and freeze for 4 hours or until solid.

Matcha Chia Pudding

SERVES: 2 PREP. TIME: 5 MINS CHILLING TIME: 4 HOURS

INGREDIENTS

2 tbsp coconut sugar

2 tsp matcha green tea powder

½ tsp vanilla extract

600 ml / 1 pint / 2 ½ cups soya milk

100 g / 3 ½ oz / ½ cup chia seeds

1 strawberry, quartered

2 sprigs mint

METHOD

- Whisk the sugar, matcha and vanilla into the milk until dissolved, then stir in the chia seeds.
- Transfer the bowl to the fridge and leave to thicken for 4 hours, stirring occasionally.
- Spoon the pudding into two glasses and top with the strawberry and mint sprigs.

Cacao Blueberry Pudding

SERVES: **4** PREP. TIME: **5 MINS** COOKING TIME: **4 HOURS**

INGREDIENTS

75 g / 2 ½ oz / ⅓ cup coconut sugar
50 g / 1 ¾ oz / ½ cup pure cacao powder
600 ml / 1 pint / 2 ½ cups soya milk
100 g / 3 ½ oz / ½ cup chia seeds
75 g / 2 ½ oz / ½ cup blueberries
1 tbsp flaked (slivered) almonds
a few sprigs mint

METHOD

- Whisk the sugar and cacao into the milk until dissolved, then stir in the chia seeds.
- Transfer the bowl to the fridge and leave to thicken for 4 hours, stirring occasionally.
- Spoon the pudding into four glasses and top with blueberries, almonds and mint sprigs.

Baked Apples

SERVES: **4** PREP. TIME: **10 MINS** COOKING TIME: **30 MINS**

INGREDIENTS

4 eating apples

4 medjool dates, stoned and chopped

50 g / 1 ¾ oz / ⅓ cup white chocolate, chopped

15 g / ½ oz / ¼ cup flaked (slivered) almonds

¼ tsp ground cinnamon

METHOD

- Preheat the oven to 180°C (160°C fan) / 350F / gas 4.
- Cut the tops off the apples and set aside, then remove the cores and transfer to a baking dish.
- Toss the dates with the chocolate, almonds and cinnamon, then pack into the apples and arrange the lids on top.
- Bake in the oven for 30 minutes or until the apples are soft.

Chocolate Coconut Truffles

MAKES: 24 PREP. TIME: 45 MINS COOKING TIME: 5 MINS CHILLING TIME: 4 HOURS 30 MINS

INGREDIENTS

FOR THE GANACHE:

225 ml / 8 fl. oz / ¾ cup canned coconut milk

300 g / 10 ½ oz / 2 cups dark chocolate (min 85% cocoa solids), finely chopped

2 tbsp coconut oil

TO DECORATE:

200 g / 7 oz / 1 ⅓ cups dark chocolate (min 85% cocoa solids), finely chopped

28 g / 1 oz / ¼ cup desiccated coconut

METHOD

- Put the coconut milk in a small saucepan with a pinch of salt and heat it gently. Meanwhile, put the chocolate and coconut oil in a mixing bowl.
- When the coconut milk starts to simmer, pour it over the chocolate in the bowl. Leave it to stand for 30 seconds, then stir gently until it forms a homogenous smooth ganache.
- Cover with cling film and chill for 4 hours or until set.
- Roll heaped teaspoons of the mixture into balls and spread them out on a plate. Chill the ganache balls in the fridge for at least 30 minutes.
- To decorate, melt the chocolate in a bain-marie or the microwave. Dip each ganache ball in melted chocolate and transfer to a sheet of greaseproof paper. Sprinkle with a little desiccated coconut then leave to set.

Blueberry Cheesecake

SERVES: 8 PREP. TIME: 45 MINS FREEZING TIME: 4 HOURS

INGREDIENTS

250 g / 9 oz / 1 ½ cups medjool dates, stoned

225 g / 8 oz / 1 ¾ cups walnuts, chopped

250 g / 9 oz / 1 ⅔ cups raw cashew nuts, soaked overnight

400 ml / 14 fl. oz / 2 cup canned coconut milk, chilled unopened

1 ½ lemons, juiced and zest finely grated

75 g / 2 ½ oz ¼ cup runny honey

150 g / 5 oz / 1 cup blueberries

edible flowers to serve

METHOD

- Soak the dates in warm water for 10 minutes, then drain and transfer to a food processor. Add the chopped walnuts and pulse until it forms a dough. Line a 20 cm (8 in) round spring-form cake tin with cling film, then press the mixture into the base.

- Drain the cashews and put them in the food processor. Open the can of coconut milk upside down and discard the thin watery layer. Scoop the thick creamy layer into the food processor and add the lemon juice, zest, honey and half the blueberries.

- Blend until very smooth, pausing to scrape down the sides occasionally. Scrape into the tin and level the top, then cover with cling film. Freeze the cheesecake for at least 4 hours.

- Remove from the freezer 20 minutes before serving. Unmould the cheesecake and garnish with the rest of the blueberries and some edible flowers.

Choco Banana Ice Lollies

MAKES: **8** PREP. TIME: **20 MINS** COOKING TIME: **4 HOURS**

INGREDIENTS

2 very ripe bananas

200 g / 7 oz / ¾ cup silken tofu

200 ml / 7 fl. oz / ¾ cup coconut milk

1 lime, juiced

75 g / 2 ½ oz / ⅓ cup coconut sugar

200 g / 7 oz / 1 ⅓ cup dark chocolate
(minimum 85% cocoa solids)

2 tbsp coconut oil

100 g / 3 ½ oz / ¾ cup walnuts, chopped

100 g / 3 ½ oz / ¾ cup freshly grated
coconut

METHOD

- Put the bananas, tofu, coconut milk, lime juice and sugar in a liquidizer and blend until smooth.

- Pour into an 8-hole ice lolly mould and add lolly sticks, then freeze for 4 hours or until solid.

- Melt the chocolate with the coconut oil in a bain-marie, stirring occasionally until smooth.

- Unmould the lollies. Dip four of the lollies in chocolate, then roll immediately in chopped walnuts. Dip the other four in chocolate and roll in coconut.

- Serve the lollies immediately or wrap in greaseproof paper and store in the freezer.

Sides & Snacks

The superfoods that are incorporated in this diet pack quite a punch, but that doesn't always prevent the occasional craving for a snack! Choosing the right kind of snack is crucial. The ideas shown in the following recipes contain all the sirt-rich components necessary and offer a range of ways to fill that odd hunger pang. There's no harm in keeping your energy up throughout the day with the occasional snack and there are some delicious options here. Nuts and medjool dates are especially good sources of the right nutrients and these sirt-rich treats can be safely snacked on without compromising the rest of the diet. What's more, these snacks are super easy to make, with the **Griddled Baby Artichokes**, **Fruity Roquefort Salad** and **Kale Chips** taking just five minutes to prepare! Side dishes are also covered in this chapter with a variety of flavoursome, sirt-packed ways in which to enhance a light meal or a bigger course. Pick and choose your favourites!

Chickpea Spinach Burgers

MAKES: **8** PREP. TIME: **10 MINS** COOKING TIME: **25 MINS**

INGREDIENTS

3 tbsp extra virgin olive oil

½ red onion, very finely chopped

2 cloves of garlic, finely chopped

1 green chilli (chili), finely chopped

1 courgette (zucchini), grated

1 tsp turmeric

400 g / 14 oz / 2 cups canned chickpeas (garbanzo beans), rinsed and drained

1 large handful baby spinach leaves

6 free-range eggs

METHOD

- Preheat the oven to 180°C (160°C fan) / 350F / gas 4 and grease an 8-hole silicone Yorkshire pudding mould with 1 tbsp of the oil.

- Heat 2 tbsp of olive oil in a frying pan and fry the onion, garlic and chilli for 4 minutes. Stir in the courgette and a pinch of salt and cook for 5 minutes or until any liquid that comes out has evaporated. Stir in the turmeric, chickpeas and spinach and take the pan off the heat.

- Lightly beat the eggs in a jug, then stir in the chickpea mixture. Fill each hole of the Yorkshire pudding mould, then transfer it to the oven.

- Bake for 15 minutes or until the burgers are cooked in the centre and golden brown on the outside.

Roasted Roots

SERVES: **4** PREP. TIME: **5 MINS** COOKING TIME: **45 MINS**

INGREDIENTS

4 tbsp extra virgin olive oil

2 tbsp light soy sauce

4 carrots, halved

8 baby beetroot, halved

2 potatoes, cut into 8 wedges

2 small parsnips, quartered

1 tbsp rosemary, chopped

coconut yogurt, to serve

METHOD

- Preheat the oven to 190°C (170°C fan) / 375F / gas 5.
- Put all of the ingredients in a freezer bag. Seal the top, then shake to coat in the oil and soy.
- Tip the vegetables into a large roasting tin then season well with salt and pepper. Roast for 45 minutes, turning occasionally, adding the rosemary 10 minutes before the end.
- Serve with coconut yogurt.

Roasted Pepper Crostini

SERVES: **4** - PREP. TIME: **35 MINS** / COOKING TIME: **20 MINS**

INGREDIENTS

3 red peppers

2 tbsp extra virgin olive oil

2 tbsp flat-leaf parsley, chopped

75 g / 2 ½ oz / ⅓ cup pickled caperberries

1 seeded wholegrain baguette, sliced on the diagonal

1 clove of garlic, halved

METHOD

- Preheat the grill to its highest setting. Grill the peppers for 20 minutes, turning occasionally, until blacked and blistered all over. Transfer the peppers to a mixing bowl and cover tightly with cling film. Leave to steam for 20 minutes.
- When the peppers are cool enough to handle, peel off the skins and tear them into strips. Dress the peppers with the oil and a pinch of salt and pepper, then toss them with the parsley and caperberries.
- Grill the baguette slices until lightly toasted, then rub the cut surfaces with the garlic clove.
- Pile the peppers and caperberries on top and serve immediately.

Hummus and Baba Ghanoush

SERVES: 4 PREP. TIME: **20 MINS** COOKING TIME: **15 MINS**

INGREDIENTS

FOR THE HUMMUS:
400 g / 14 oz / 2 ⅔ cups canned chickpeas (garbanzo beans), drained

6 tbsp extra virgin olive oil, plus extra for drizzling

1 tbsp tahini paste

1 lemon, juiced

1 clove of garlic, crushed

¼ tsp ground cumin

1 tbsp flat-leaf parsley, chopped

Cayenne pepper, for sprinkling

FOR THE BABA GHANOUSH:
1 large aubergine (eggplant)

4 tbsp extra virgin olive oil

½ lemon, juiced

1 tbsp tahini paste

1 clove of garlic, crushed

½ red onion, finely chopped

2 tbsp flat-leaf parsley, finely chopped

METHOD

- To make the hummus, put the chickpeas, oil, tahini, lemon juice, garlic and cumin in a food processor. Blend to a smooth purée, then season to taste with salt and pepper.
- Spoon into a bowl, drizzle with oil and sprinkle with parsley and Cayenne pepper.
- To make the Baba ghanoush, cook the aubergine under a hot grill until the skin is black and blistered all over. Leave to cool a little, then cut in half and scoop out the flesh into a sieve. Press down with the back of a spoon to release as much liquid as possible, then finely chop the flesh.
- Transfer the chopped aubergine to a bowl, stir in the rest of the ingredients and season to taste with salt and pepper.

Chicken Summer Rolls

MAKES: **12** PREP. TIME: **15 MINS** CHILLING TIME: **1 HOUR**

INGREDIENTS

8 rice paper wrappers

8 soft lettuce leaves

2 cold roast chicken breasts, sliced

1 red pepper, deseeded and sliced

1 red onion, halved and sliced

¼ cucumber, julienned

75 g / 2 ½ oz / 2 ¼ cups pea shoots

FOR THE DIPPING SAUCE:

2 tbsp caster sugar

2 limes, juiced

2 tbsp fish sauce

1 red chilli (chili), sliced

½ garlic clove, finely chopped

METHOD

- First make the dipping sauce. Stir the sugar into the lime juice until it dissolves, then stir in the fish sauce, chilli and garlic. Taste the dressing and adjust the levels of sweet, sour and salty, then set aside to infuse.
- Dip the first rice paper wrapper in a bowl of cold water, then lay it out on a clean chopping board. Lay a lettuce leaf on top and add some chicken, pepper, onion, cucumber and pea shoots.
- Fold over the bottom edge of the wrapper, then roll it up to enclose the filling, leaving the top edge open.
- Repeat with the rest of the ingredients to form eight rolls, then serve immediately with the dipping sauce.

Griddled Baby Artichokes

SERVES: 4 PREP. TIME: 5 MINS COOKING TIME: 15 MINS

INGREDIENTS

4 baby artichokes

1 lemon, juiced

2 tbsp extra virgin olive oil

METHOD

- Preheat the oven to 190°C (170°C fan) / 375F / gas 5.
- Cut the spiky ends off each artichoke petal with a pair of scissors, then peel the stems. Cut them in half and douse liberally with lemon juice to prevent any discolouration.
- Heat an oven-proof griddle pan on the hob until smoking hot. Rub the artichokes all over with oil and season with salt and pepper, then arrange cut side down on the griddle pan.
- Transfer the griddle pan to the oven and roast for 15 minutes or until tender to the point of a knife.

Pear, Walnut and Rocket Salad

SERVES: **4** PREP. TIME: **10 MINS** COOKING TIME: **0 MINS**

INGREDIENTS

75 g / 2 ½ oz / 2 ¼ cups rocket (arugula)

2 tbsp extra virgin olive oil

1 lemon, juiced

4 ripe pears

100 g / 3 ½ oz / ¾ cup walnuts, roughly chopped

2 tbsp sesame seeds

METHOD

- Toss the rocket with the oil, half of the lemon juice and a pinch of salt and arrange on four plates.
- Slice the pears and douse with the rest of the lemon juice to stop them from discolouring, then arrange on top of the rocket.
- Scatter over the walnuts and sesame seeds and serve immediately.

Superfood Salad

SERVES: **4** PREP. TIME: **15 MINS** COOKING TIME: **0 MINS**

INGREDIENTS

75 ml / 2 ½ fl. oz / ⅓ cup extra virgin olive oil

1 lemon, juiced

1 clove of garlic, sliced

200 g / 7 oz / 4 cups curly kale, stems removed and chopped

6 radishes, thinly sliced

50 g / 1 ¾ oz / ½ cup walnuts, roughly chopped

75 g / 2 ½ oz / ⅓ cup dried sour cherries

75 g / 2 ½ oz / ⅓ cup feta cheese, crumbled

METHOD

- Whisk the oil with the lemon juice and a pinch of salt, then add the garlic and leave to infuse for 10 minutes. Remove and discard the garlic.

- Toss the kale with the dressing, ensuring it is evenly covered, then divide it between four bowls.

- Scatter over the radishes, walnuts, sour cherries and feta then serve immediately.

Kale Chips

SERVES: **4** PREP. TIME: **5 MINS** COOKING TIME: **30 MINS**

INGREDIENTS

2 tbsp extra virgin olive oil

100 g / 3 ½ oz / 3 cups curly kale, washed and dried

¼ tsp chilli (chili) flakes

METHOD

- Preheat the oven to 150°C (130°C fan) / 300F / gas 2.
- Massage the oil into the kale and spread it out in a roasting tin.
- Sprinkle with chilli flakes and season lightly with salt, then roast for 30 minutes, stirring every 10 minutes.

Fruity Roquefort Salad

SERVES: 4 PREP. TIME: 5 MINS COOKING TIME: 0 MINS

INGREDIENTS

1 curly endive lettuce, torn

75 g / 2 ½ oz / 2 ¼ cups rocket (arugula)

8 fresh figs, quartered

150 g / 5 ½ oz / 1 cup black seedless grapes, halved

150 g / 5 ½ oz / 1 cup blueberries

½ pomegranate, seeds only

150 g / 5 ½ oz / ⅔ cup Roquefort

50 ml / 1 ¾ fl. oz / ¼ cup balsamic glaze

4 tbsp extra virgin olive oil

METHOD

- Divide the lettuce and rocket between four plates.
- Top with the figs, grapes, blueberries and pomegranate seeds.
- Crumble over the Roquefort then drizzle with balsamic glaze and olive oil. Serve immediately.

Marinated Tofu Skewers

SERVES: 4 PREP. TIME: **35 MINS** COOKING TIME: **8 MINS**

INGREDIENTS

350 g / 12 oz / 1 ½ cups firm tofu, cubed

3 tbsp extra virgin olive oil

1 lemon, sliced

2 cloves of garlic, squashed

2 sprigs rosemary

1 small bunch thyme

1 courgette (zucchini), halved and thickly sliced

24 cherry tomatoes

2 tbsp flat-leaf parsley, chopped

2 tbsp lovage, chopped

METHOD

- Put the tofu in a large freezer bag with the oil, lemon, garlic, rosemary and thyme. Leave to marinate for at least 30 minutes.
- Meanwhile, soak eight wooden skewers in water to prevent them burning.
- Remove the tofu from the marinade and thread it onto the skewers with the courgette and tomatoes.
- Heat a griddle pan until smoking hot then season the skewers with salt and cook for 4 minutes on each side or until nicely marked and hot throughout.

Index

PARSNIP
Roasted Roots, 65

PEA SHOOTS
Chicken Summer Rolls, 69

PEAR
Pear, Walnut and Rocket Salad, 72

PEAS
Rice and Tofu Congee, 34

PEPPERS
Chicken Summer Rolls, 69
Chicken Udon Stir-fry, 36
Roast Chicken with Quinoa, 31
Roasted Pepper Crostini, 67
Vegetable Buckwheat Pizza, 43

PINE NUTS
Halibut with Kale and Capers, 30

PINEAPPLE
Tropical Smoothie, 20

PISTACHIO NUTS
Whipped Cacao Mousse, 51

PLAICE
Plaice with Avocado Salsa, 39

POMEGRANATE
Fruity Roquefort Salad, 76
Pomegranate Chia Verrines, 49

PUMPKIN SEEDS
Cacao and Banana Porridge, 22
Stuffed Sweet Potato, 41

QUINOA, RED
Chicken Udon Stir-fry, 36
Roast Chicken with Quinoa, 31

RADISH
Superfood Salad, 73

RASPBERRIES
Raw Raspberry Tarts, 52

RED CABBAGE
Soba Noodle Salad, 42

RED CURRY PASTE
Chicken Udon Stir-fry, 36

RICE, RED
Rice and Tofu Congee, 34

RICE PAPER WRAPPERS
Chicken Summer Rolls, 69

RICE WINE VINEGAR
Soba Noodle Salad, 42

ROCKET (ARUGULA)
Fruity Roquefort Salad, 76
Pear, Walnut and Rocket Salad, 72

ROQUEFORT
Fruity Roquefort Salad, 76

SALMON
Citrus-cured Salmon on Rye, 35

SEEDED BAGUETTE, WHOLEGRAIN
Roasted Pepper Crostini, 67

SESAME OIL
Soba Noodle Salad, 42

SESAME SEEDS
Pear, Walnut and Rocket Salad, 72
Soba Noodle Salad, 42

SOY SAUCE
Chicken Udon Stir-fry, 36
Rice and Tofu Congee, 34
Roasted Roots, 65
Soba Noodle Salad, 42
Stuffed Sweet Potato, 41

SOYA MILK
Avocado Smoothie Bowl, 19
Cacao and Banana Porridge, 22
Cacao Blueberry Pudding, 56
Chia Granola Pots, 27
Chia Panna Cotta, 15
Layered Buckwheat Porridge, 26
Matcha Chia Pudding, 54
Pomegranate Chia Verrines, 49
Super Green Juice, 25
Tropical Smoothie, 20

SOYA YOGURT
Buckwheat Goji Granola, 18
Vegetable Buckwheat Pizza, 43

SPINACH
Chicken Udon Stir-fry, 36

STRAWBERRIES
Berry Ice Lollies, 53
Buckwheat Goji Granola, 18
Chia Panna Cotta, 15
Matcha Chia Pudding, 54
Pomegranate Chia Verrines, 49

SUNFLOWER SEEDS
Buckwheat Goji Granola, 18

SWEET POTATO
Stuffed Sweet Potato, 41

TAHINI PASTE
Hummus and Baba Ghanoush, 68

TOFU
Berry Ice Lollies, 53
Choco Banana Ice Lollies, 61
Marinated Tofu Skewers, 77
Rice and Tofu Congee, 34
Whipped Cacao Mousse, 51

UDON NOODLES, WHOLEWHEAT
Chicken Udon Stir-fry, 36

VEGETABLE STOCK
Kale and Lovage Soup, 44
Rice and Tofu Congee, 34
Squash and Chickpea Soup, 33

WALNUTS
Blueberry and Walnut Muffins, 17
Blueberry Cheesecake, 60
Buckwheat Goji Granola, 18
Chia Granola Pots, 27
Choco Banana Ice Lollies, 61
Pear, Walnut and Rocket Salad, 72
Raw Raspberry Tarts, 52
Stuffed Sweet Potato, 41
Superfood Salad, 73
Vegetable Buckwheat Pizza, 43
Walnut Brownies, 48

WALNUT OIL
Whipped Cacao Mousse, 51

WHITE WINE
Halibut with Kale and Capers, 30

YELLOW CURRY PASTE
Rice and Tofu Congee, 34